Plugging the Gaps

MANUALS

100 Improvisations which may be stretched or shrunk to suit the occasion

Kevin Mayhew

We hope you enjoy the music in this book.
Further copies of this and our many other books are available
from your local music shop or Christian bookshop.

In case of difficulty, please contact the publisher direct by writing to:

The Sales Department
KEVIN MAYHEW LTD
Buxhall
Stowmarket
Suffolk IP14 3BW

Phone 01449 737978
Fax 01449 737834
E-mail info@kevinmayhewltd.com

Please ask for our complete catalogue of outstanding Church Music.

First published in Great Britain in 2000 by Kevin Mayhew Ltd.

ISBN 1 84003 633 8
ISMN M 57004 766 6
Catalogue No: 1400264

0 1 2 3 4 5 6 7 8 9

Cover design: Jonathan Stroulger
Music editor and setter: Kate Gallaher
Proof reader: Sally Gough

Printed and bound in Great Britain

Contents

C MAJOR

Interlude 1

Rosalie Bonighton

To repeat or
D.C. al Fine
To continue
rall.
alternative Fine

C MAJOR

Interlude 2

Andrew Fletcher

Interlude 3

Richard Lloyd

To Fred and Lilian Brockman

Interlude 4

Malcolm McKelvey

Interlude 5

Alan Rees

Interlude 6

Quentin Thomas

C MINOR

Interlude 7

David Terry

C MINOR

Interlude 8

Colin Mawby

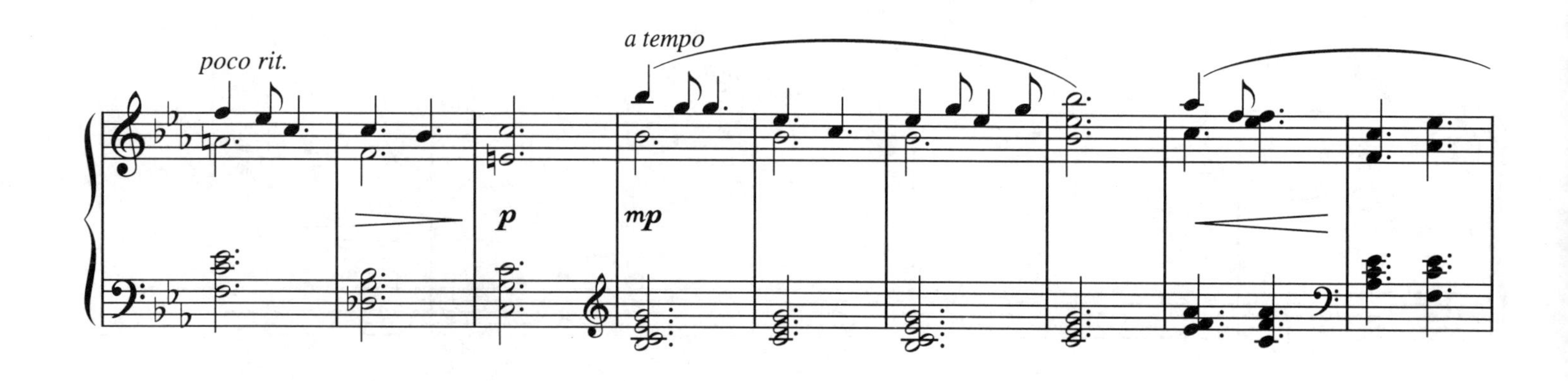

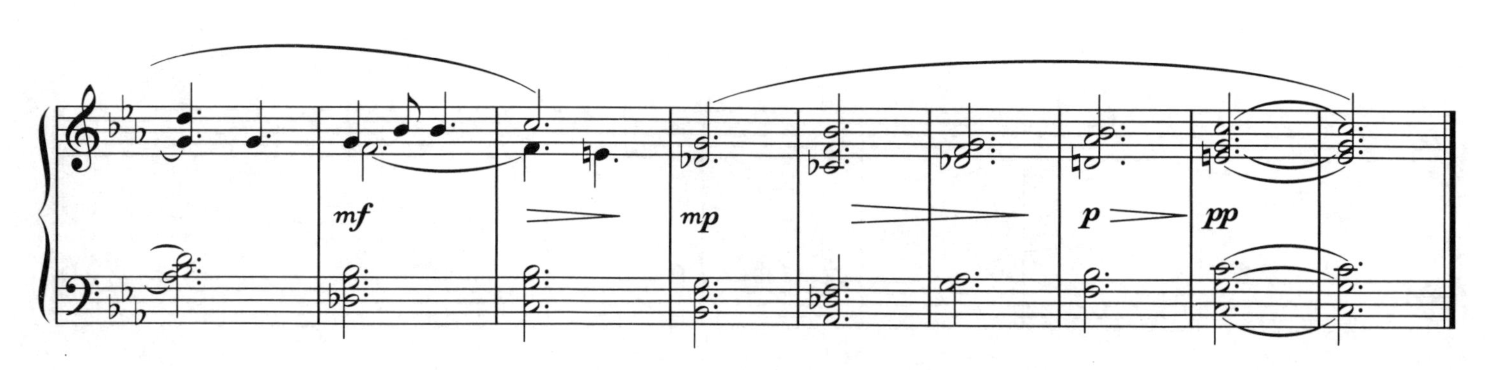

Interlude 9

Richard Lloyd

Interlude 10

Andrew Moore

C MINOR

Interlude 11

Stanley Vann

C MINOR

To Keri Dexter

C♯ MINOR

Interlude 12

Malcolm McKelvey

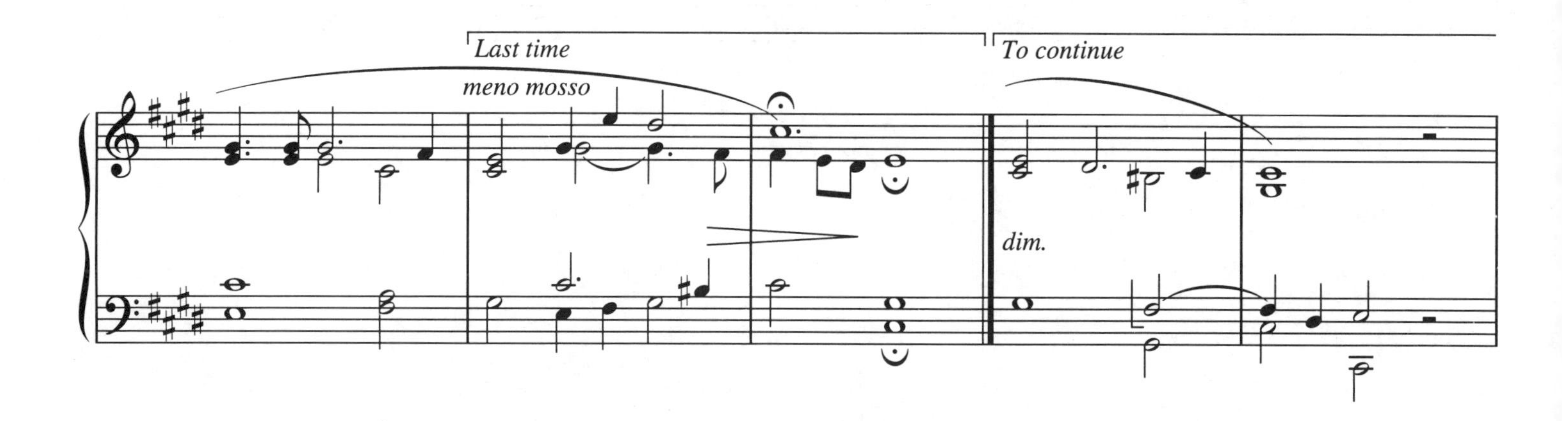

Interlude 13

Alan Rees

D MAJOR

Interlude 14

John Marsh

Interlude 15

June Nixon

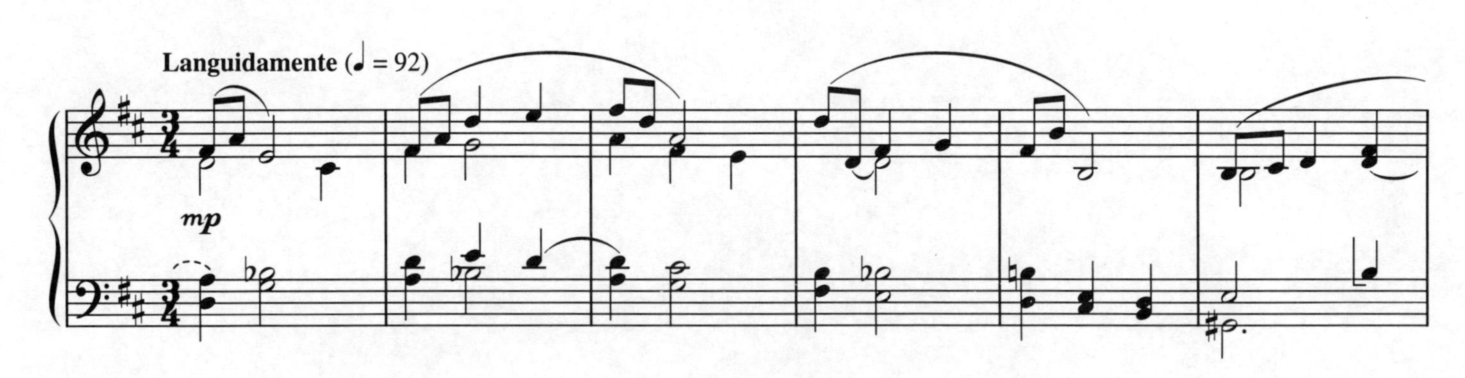

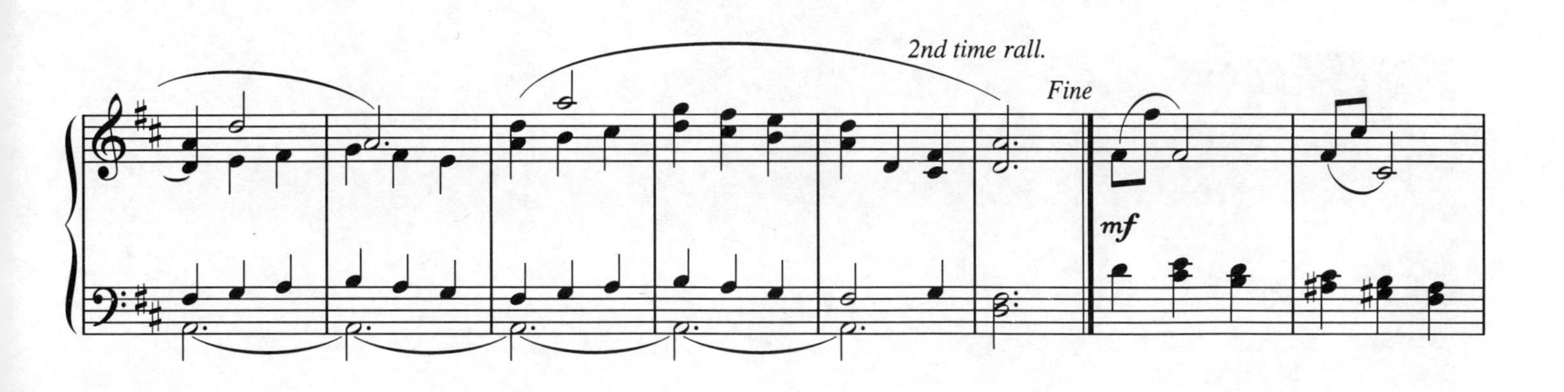

For Katharine and Maurice

D MAJOR

Interlude 16

Betty Roe

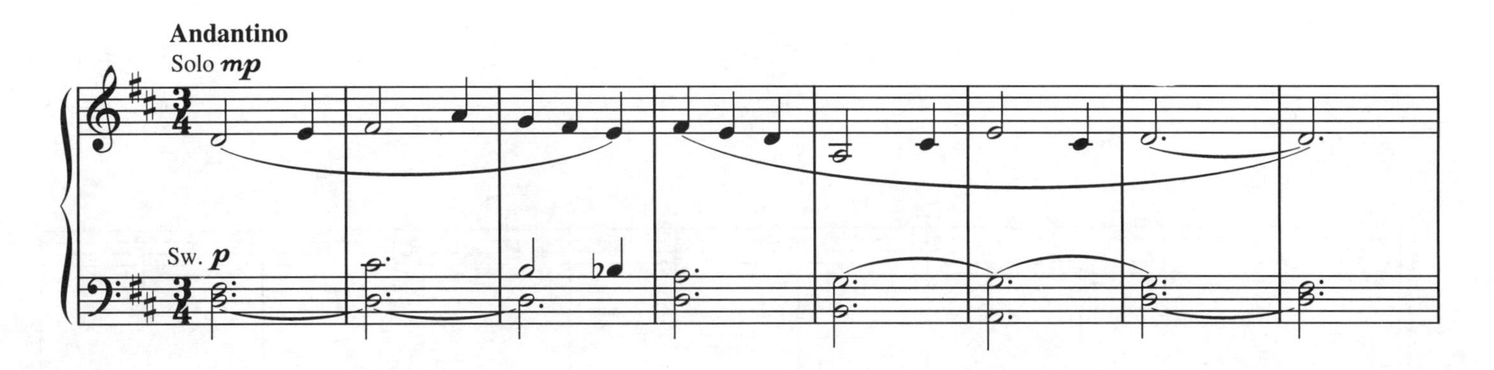

Interlude 17

Robert Jones

D MAJOR

Interlude 18

David Terry

D MAJOR

Interlude 19

Norman Warren

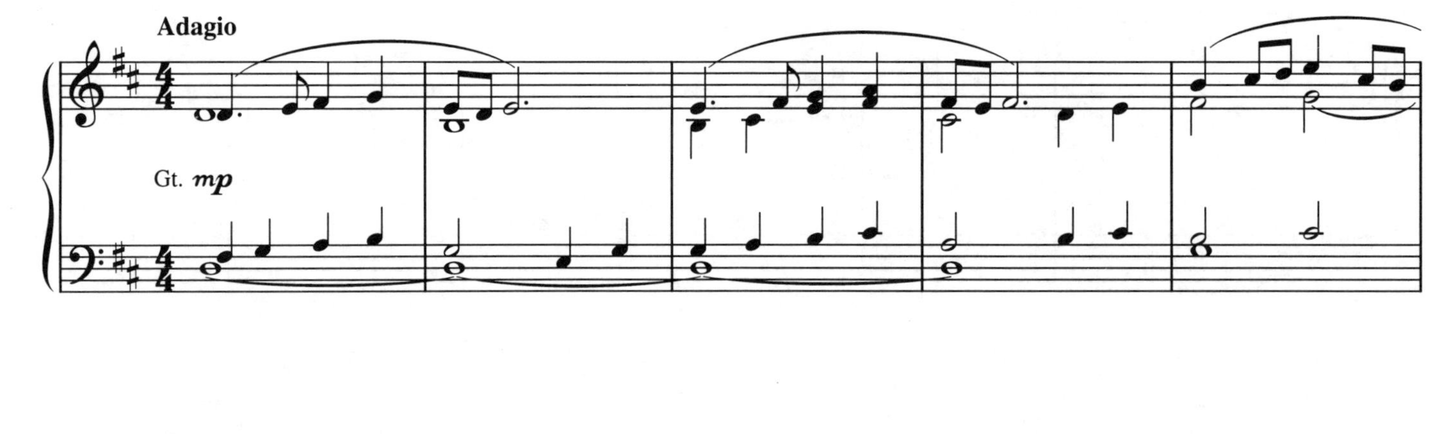

D MAJOR

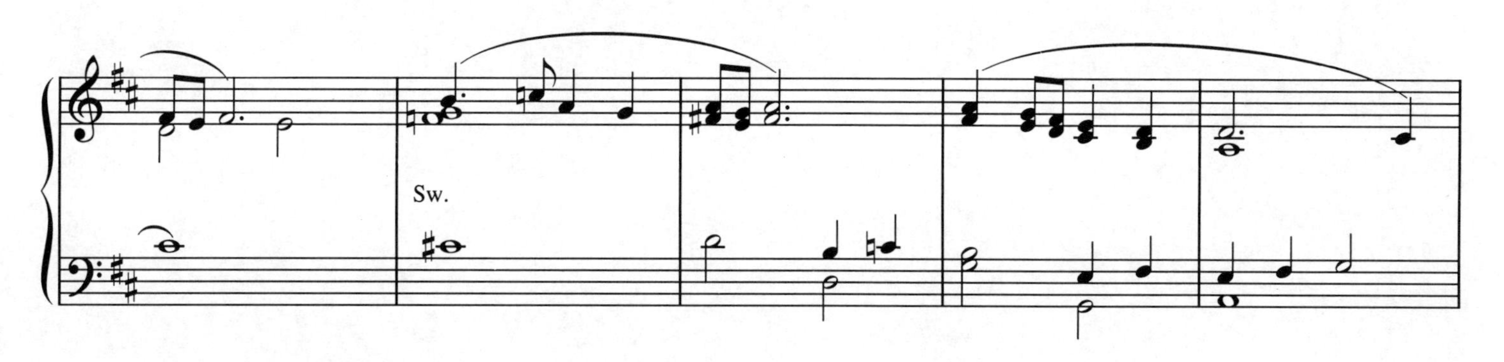
Sw.

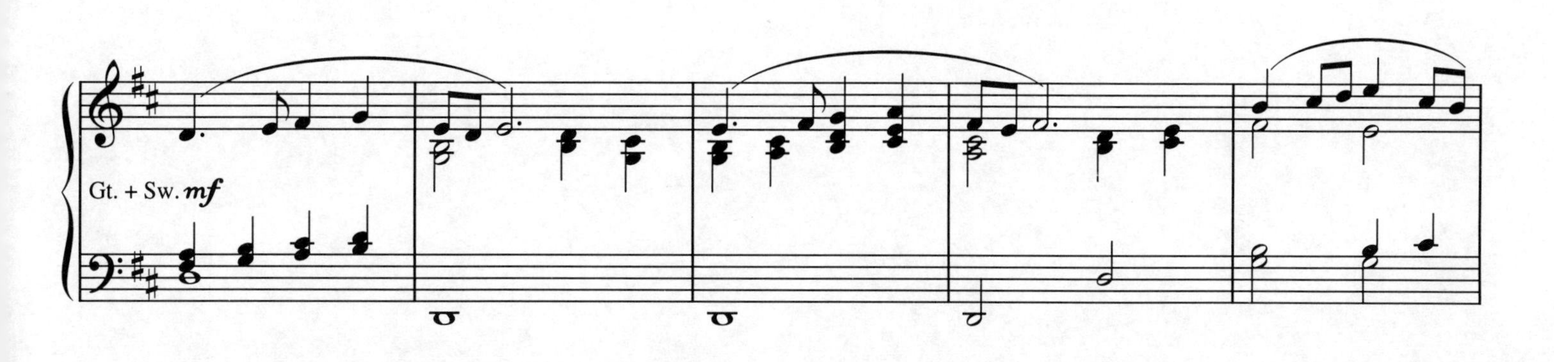
Gt. + Sw. mf

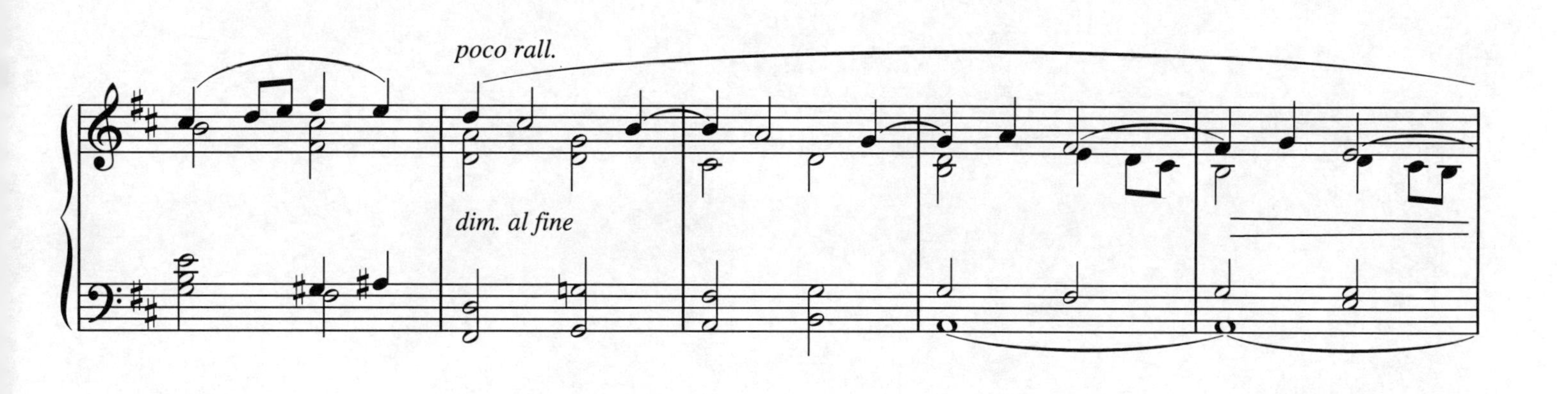
poco rall.
dim. al fine

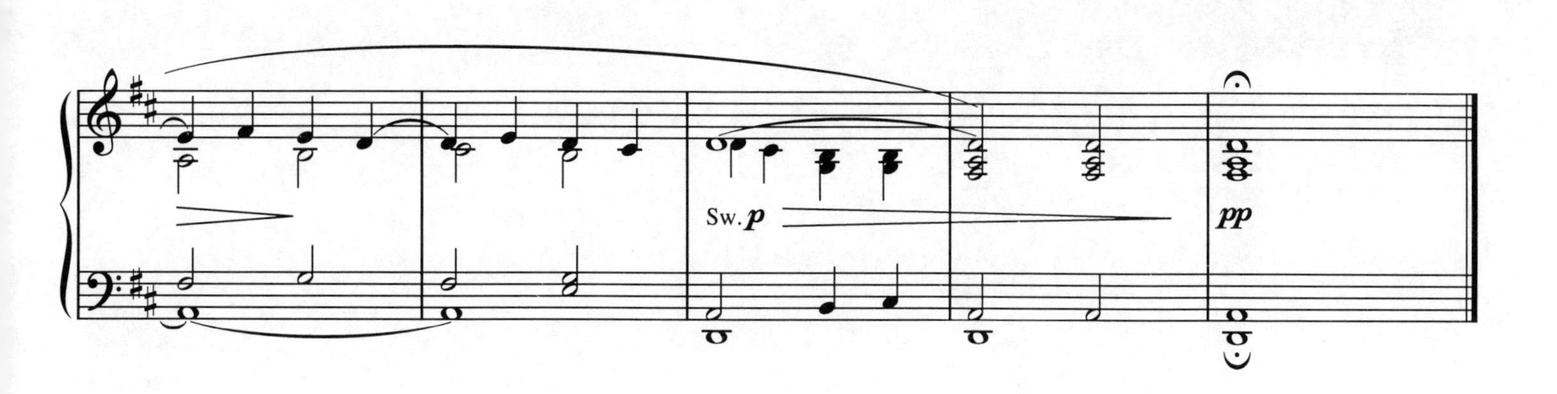
Sw. p
pp

Interlude 20

Andrew Wright

D MINOR

Interlude 21

Andrew Fletcher

mf
mp
1.
2.
D.S. al Fine
p
p
mp

D MINOR

Interlude 22

Richard Lloyd

To John Wade

D MINOR

Interlude 23

Malcolm McKelvey

Interlude 24

Andrew Moore

Interlude 25

Alan Rees

E♭ MAJOR

Interlude 26

Rosalie Bonighton

poco rall.
Fine
a tempo
Sw.
poco rall.
D.C. (or D.S.) al Fine

E♭ MAJOR

Interlude 27

June Nixon

To Mum

Interlude 28

Betty Roe

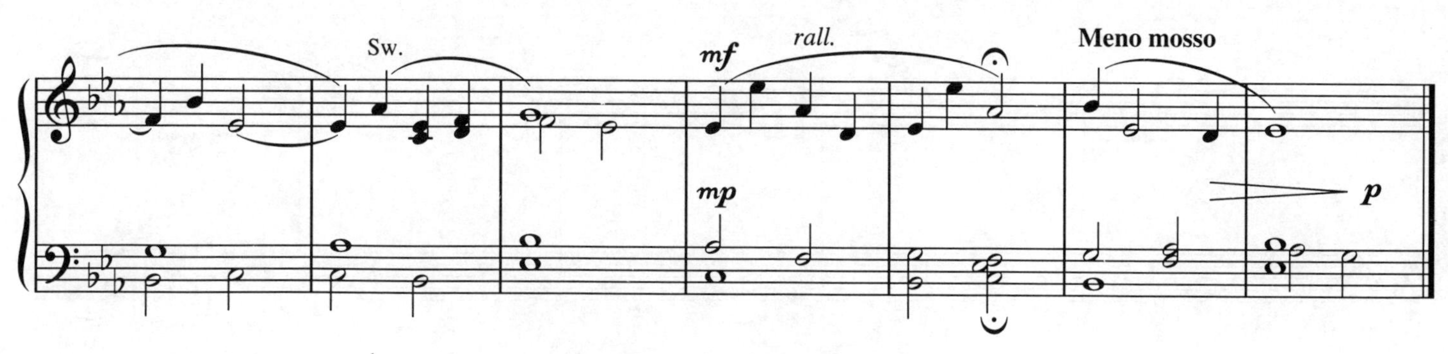

E♭ MAJOR

Interlude 29

Robert Jones

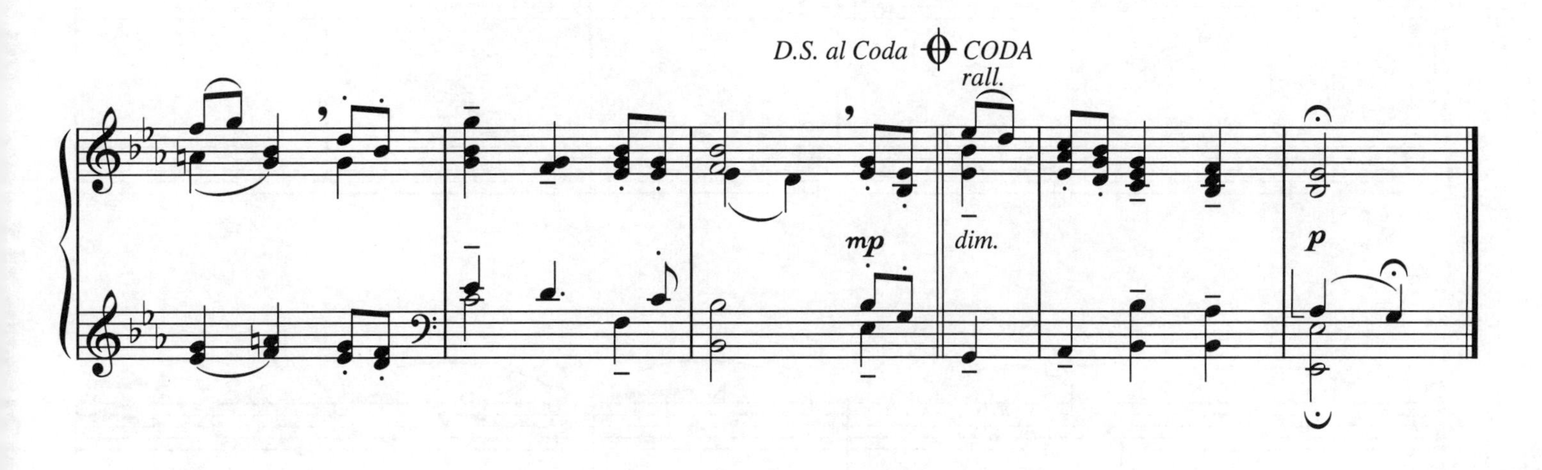
D.S. al Coda
CODA
rall.
mp
dim.
p

E♭ MAJOR

Interlude 30

Norman Warren

Gt. + Sw.
mf

Sw. p
pp

E♭ MAJOR

Interlude 31

Quentin Thomas

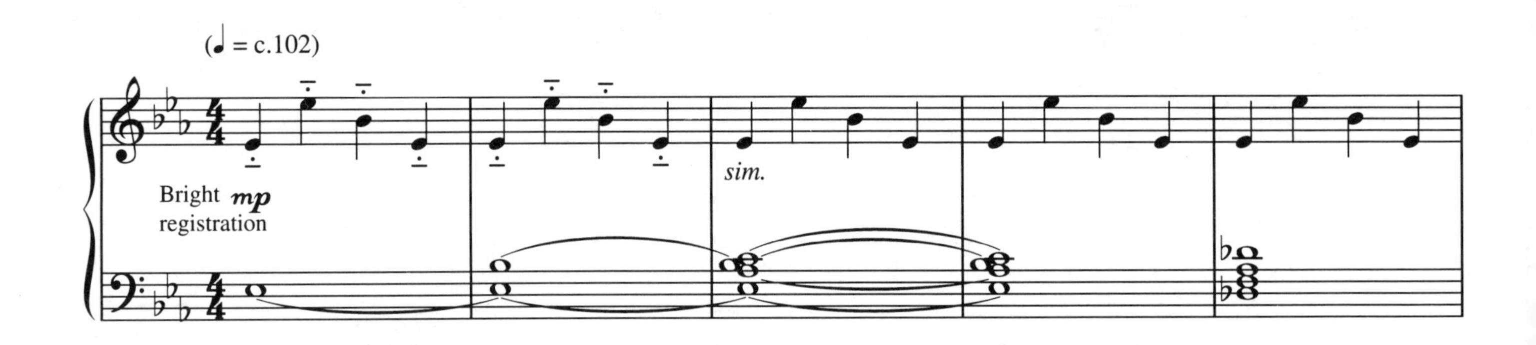

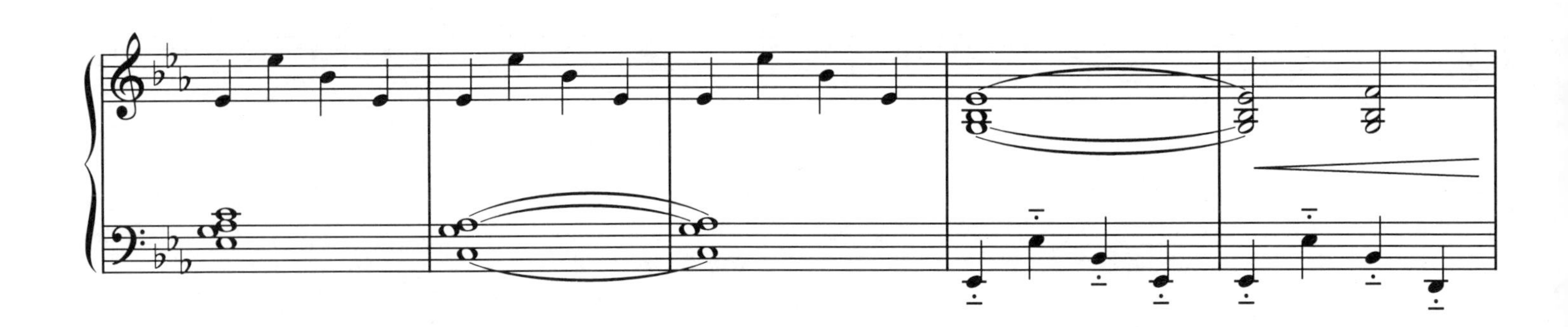

poco rall.
a tempo

poco rall.
a tempo
sim.

E MAJOR

Interlude 32

Rosalie Bonighton

To continue
mp
2nd time D.C.

E MAJOR

Interlude 33

Andrew Fletcher

Interlude 34

Quentin Thomas

E MAJOR

Interlude 35

June Nixon

E MAJOR

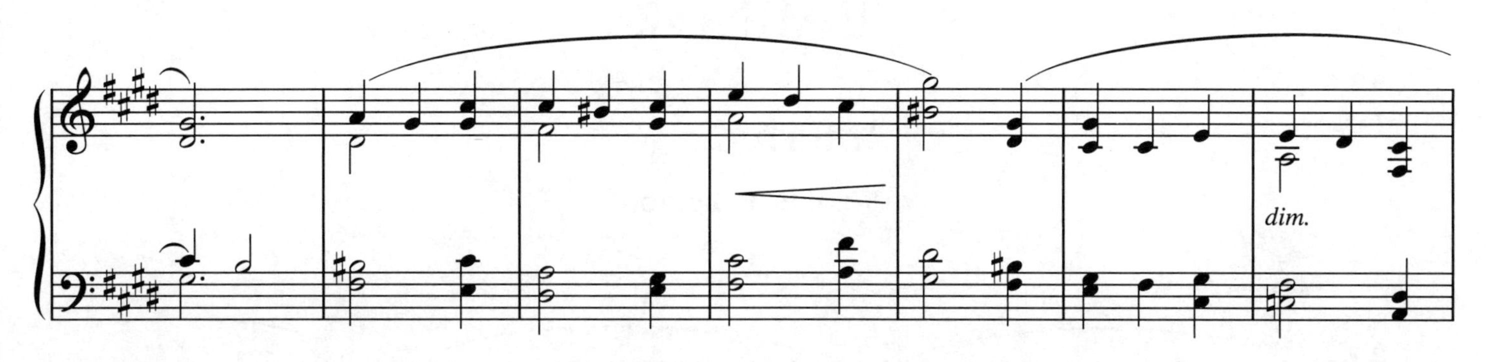
dim.

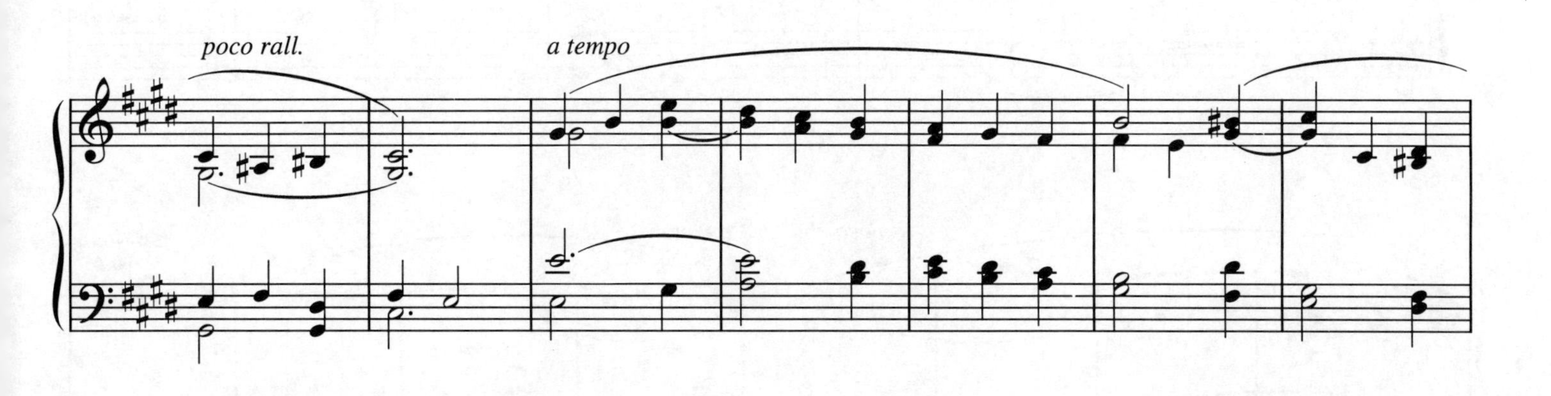
poco rall.
a tempo

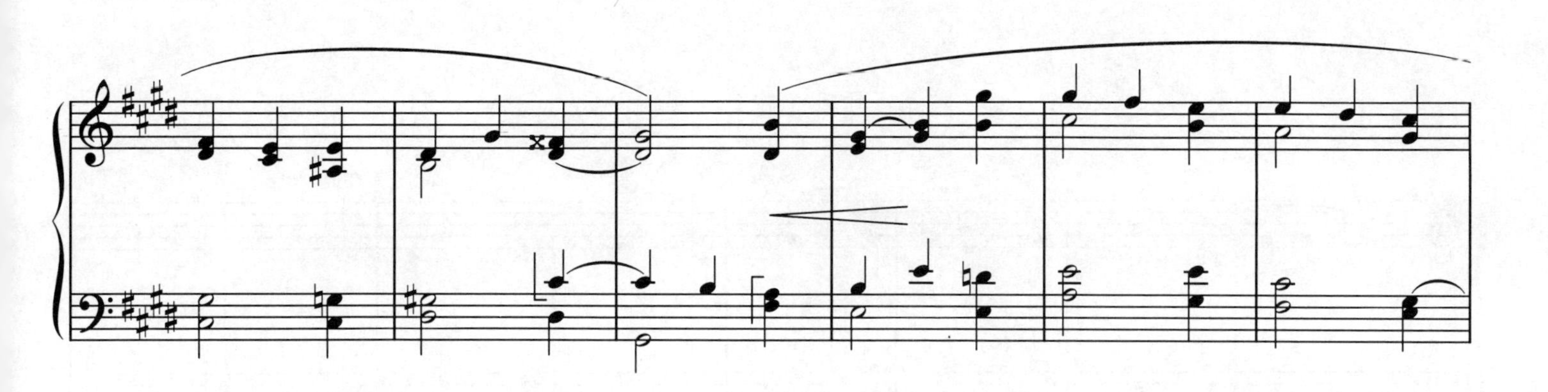

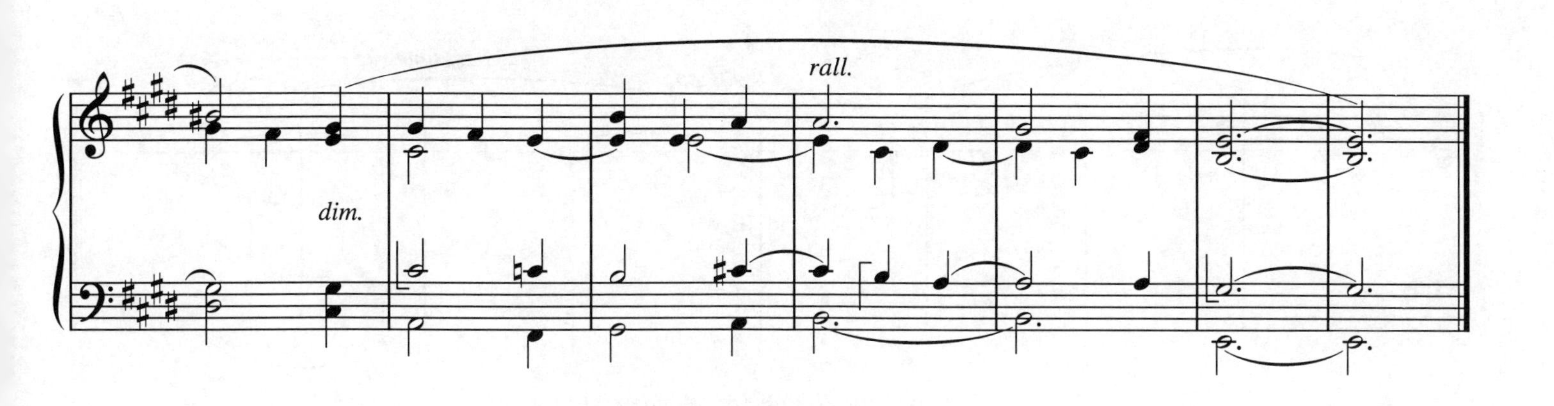
rall.
dim.

E MINOR

Interlude 36

Rosalie Bonighton

E MINOR

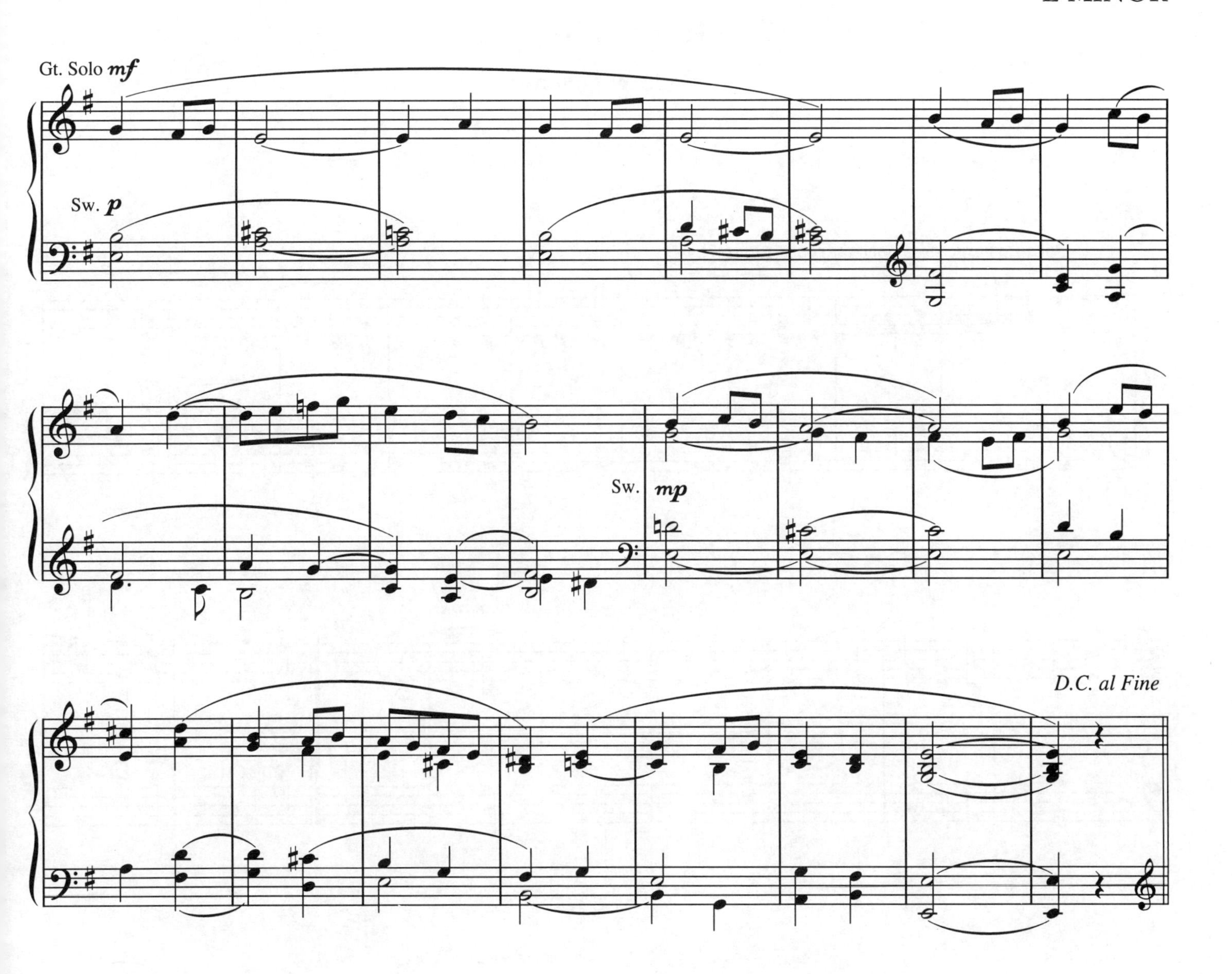
Gt. Solo mf
Sw. p
Sw. mp
D.C. al Fine

E MINOR

Interlude 37

Andrew Fletcher

E MINOR

Interlude 38

Richard Lloyd

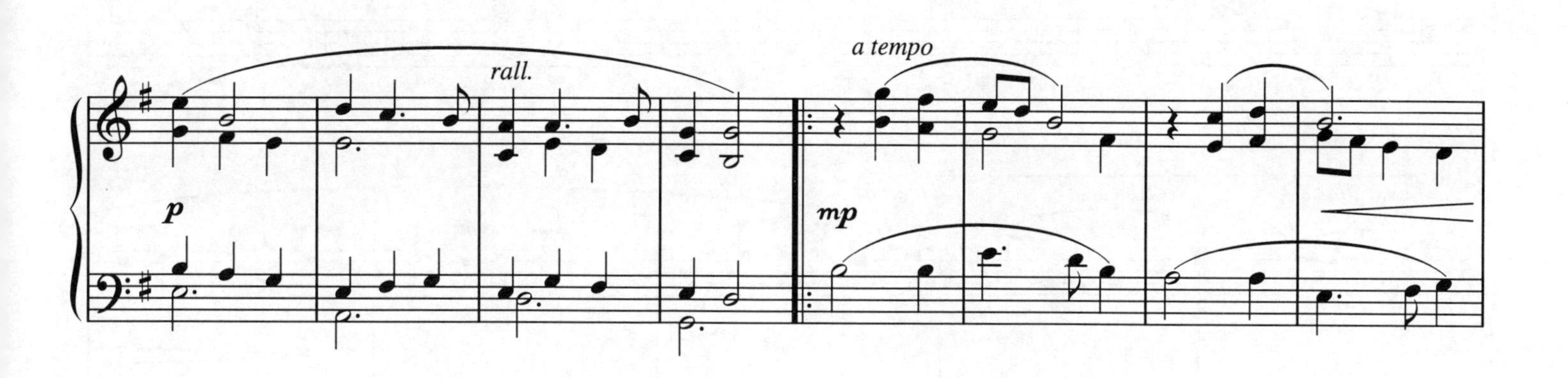

E MINOR

To Fr. Michael Cozens

Interlude 39

Malcolm McKelvey

Interlude 40

Alan Rees

E MINOR

Interlude 41

Richard Lloyd

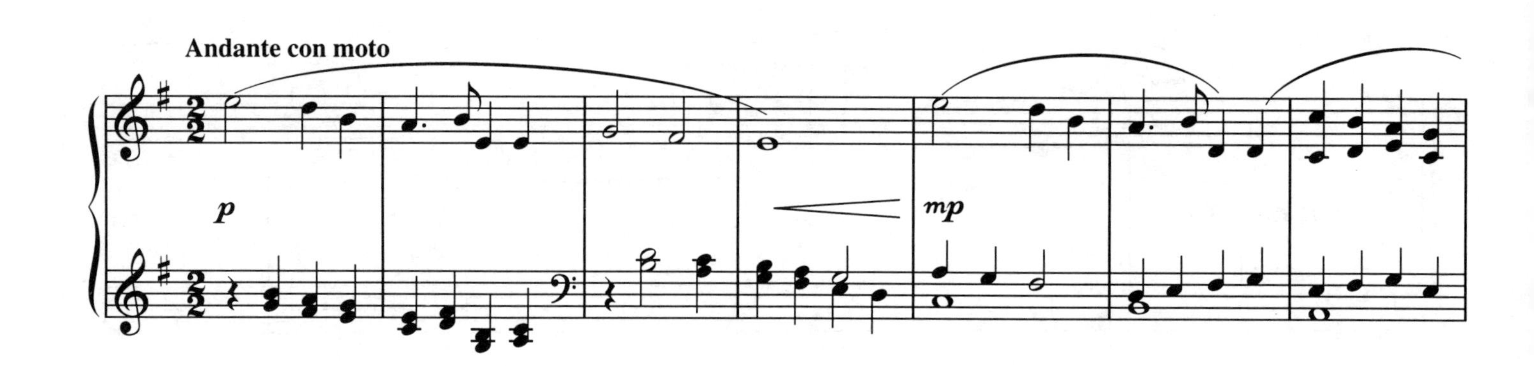

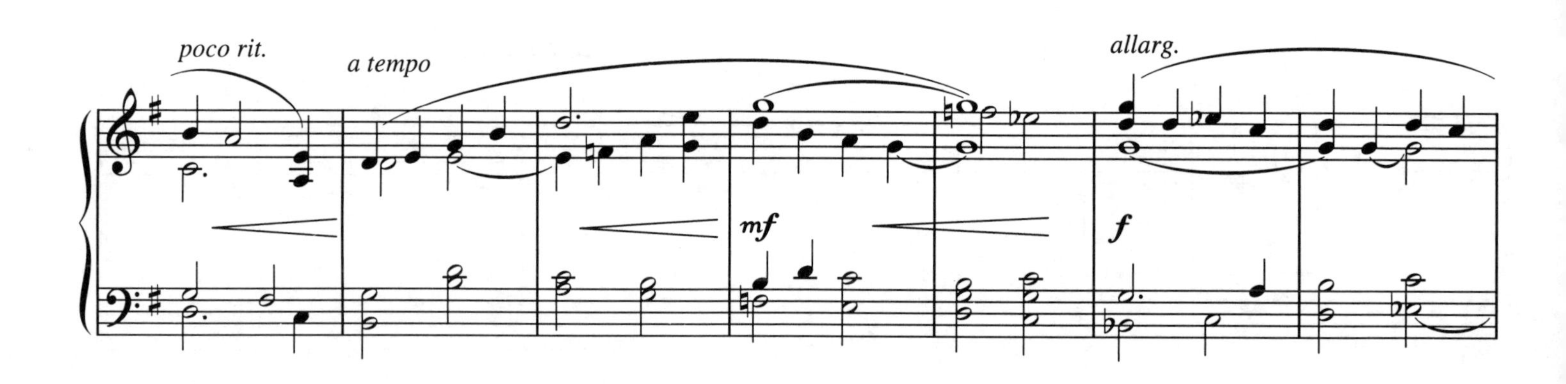

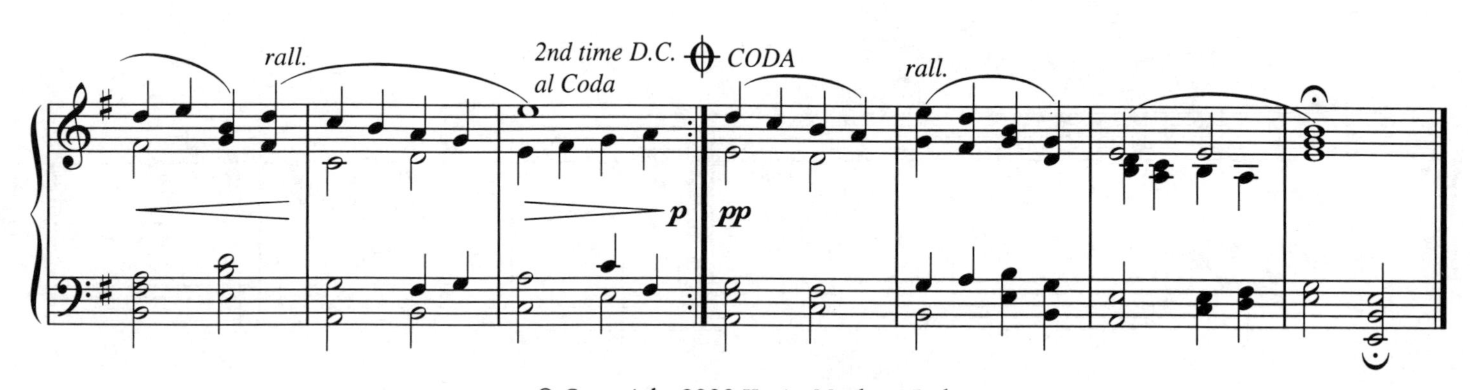

F MAJOR

Interlude 42

Colin Hand

F MAJOR

Interlude 43

Colin Mawby

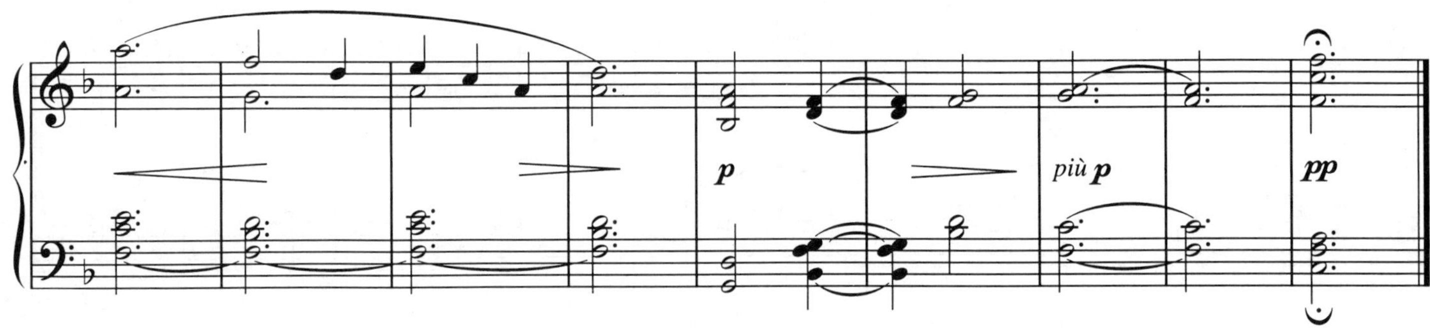

Interlude 44

Andrew Moore

F MAJOR

Interlude 45

David Terry

Interlude 46

Stanley Vann

Interlude 47

Michael Higgins

Interlude 48

David Terry

F MAJOR

Interlude 49

Elizabeth Hill

rit.
p

F MINOR

Interlude 50

Colin Hand

decresc.
mp
mp
p
rall.

F MINOR

Interlude 51

Colin Mawby

F MINOR

Interlude 52

David Terry

F MINOR

Interlude 53

Elizabeth Hill

mp

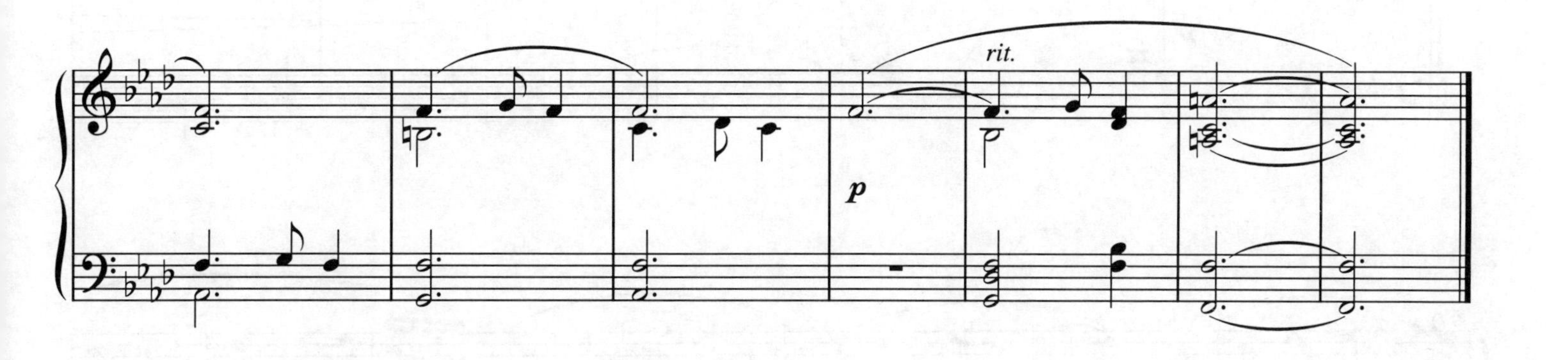
rit.
p

F♯ MINOR

Interlude 54

Stanley Vann

F♯ MINOR

Interlude 55

Richard Lloyd

F♯ MINOR

Interlude 56

Andrew Moore

G MAJOR

Interlude 57

Colin Mawby

Interlude 58

Colin Hand

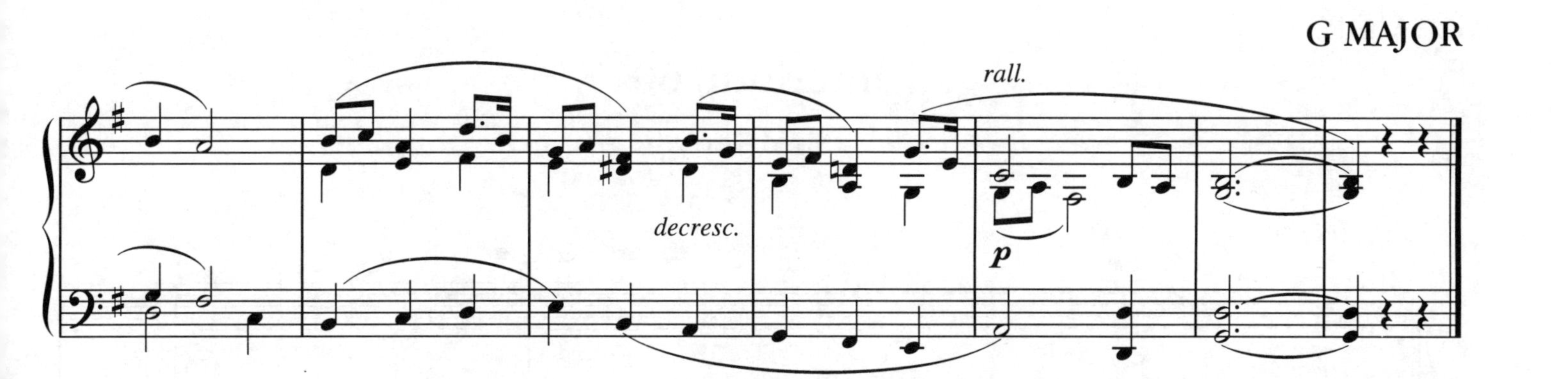

Interlude 59

Andrew Moore

Interlude 60

David Terry

Interlude 61

Stanley Vann

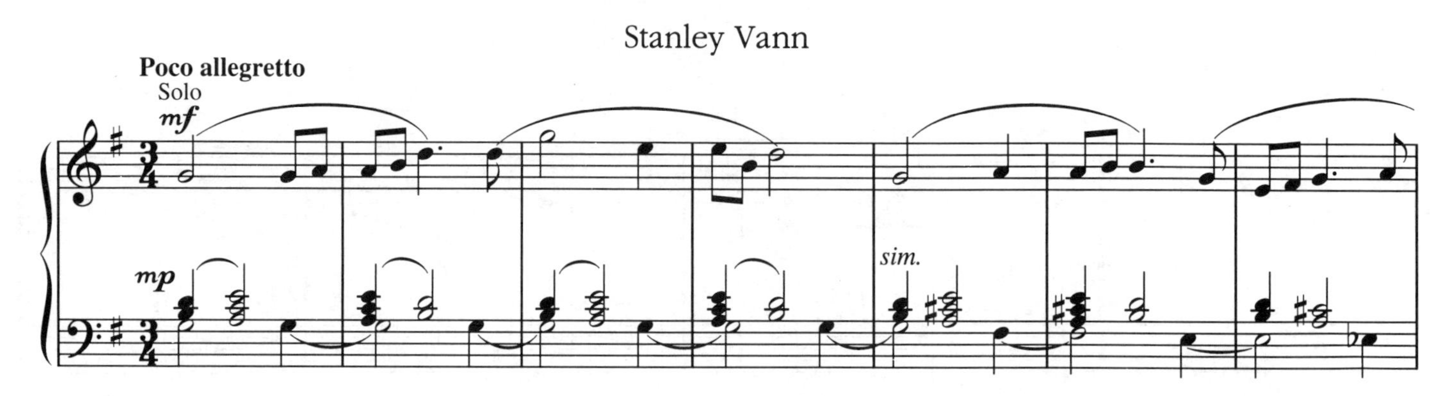

G MAJOR

poco rit.
a tempo
sim.

mp

rit.
a tempo
mf
mp

meno mosso
mp
rit.
p
dim.

Interlude 62

Elizabeth Hill

mf
poco meno mosso
p

Interlude 63

Michael Higgins

Interlude 64

Andrew Wright

G MAJOR

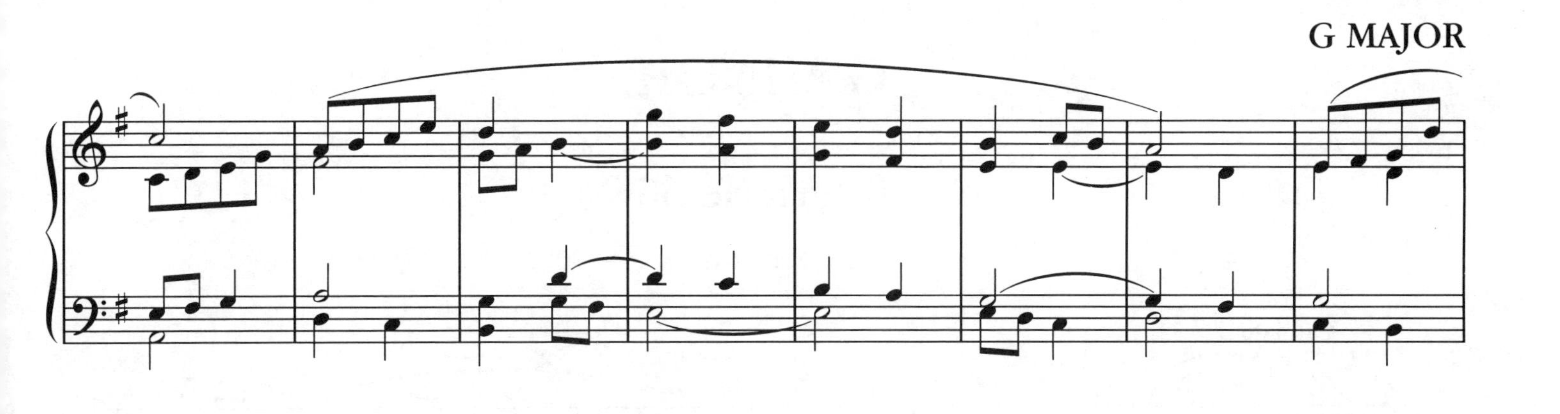

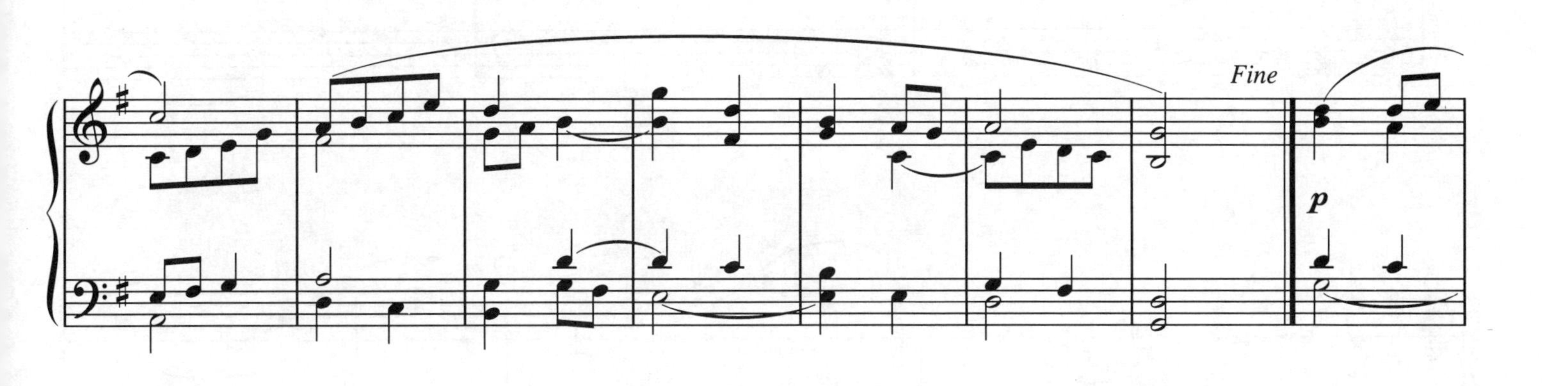

Fine
p

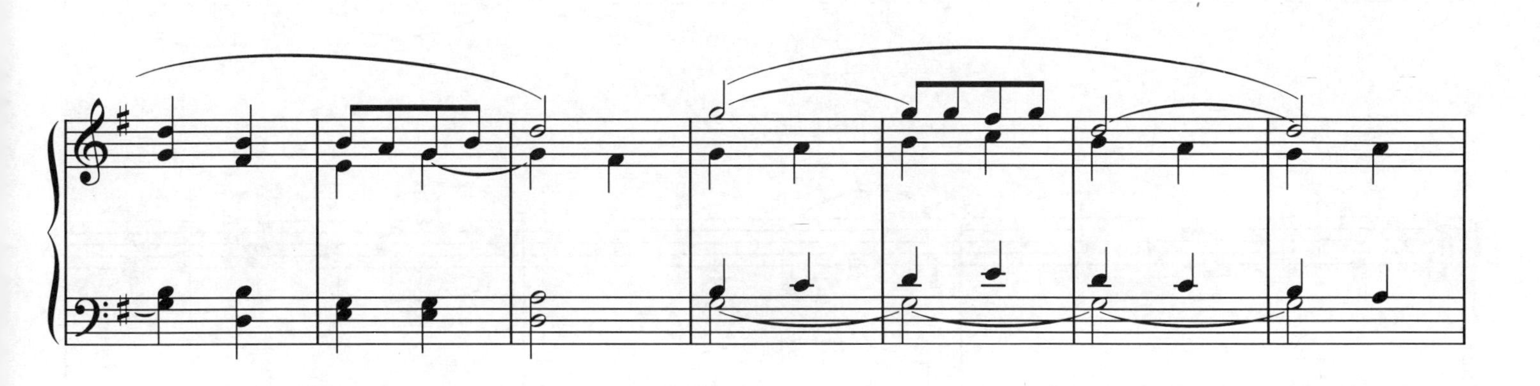

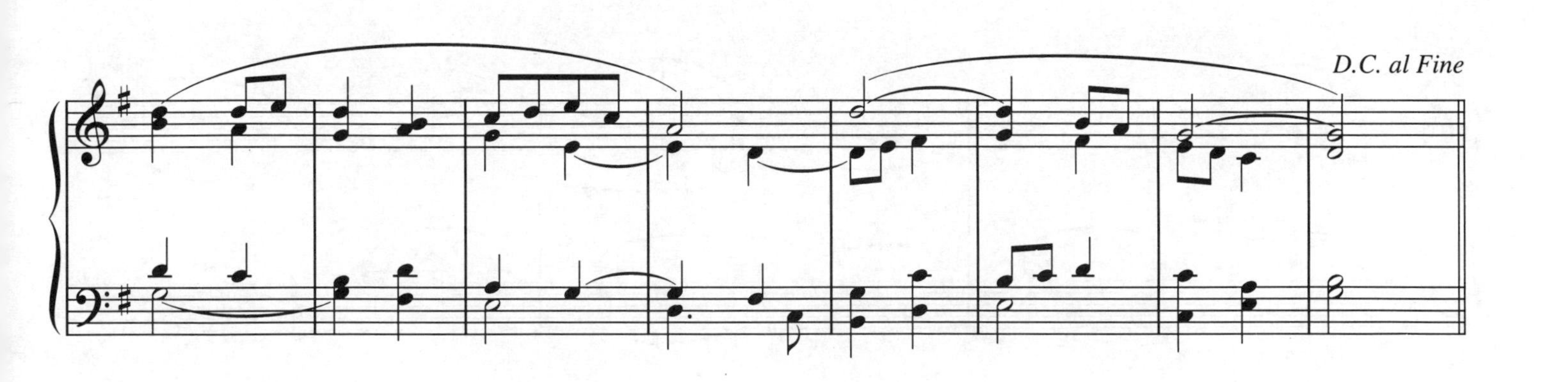

D.C. al Fine

G MINOR

Interlude 65

Robert Jones

f
p

mp

rall.
cresc.
dim.
pp

G MINOR

Interlude 66

Norman Warren

Gt.

rall.
dim.
Sw.
p
pp

G MINOR

Interlude 67

Rosalie Bonighton

* The Last time bar may follow (with a rall.)

G MINOR

G MINOR

Interlude 68

June Nixon

Poco più mosso
mf
D.C. al Fine

G MINOR

Interlude 69

Norman Warren

Gt.

Gt. + Sw.

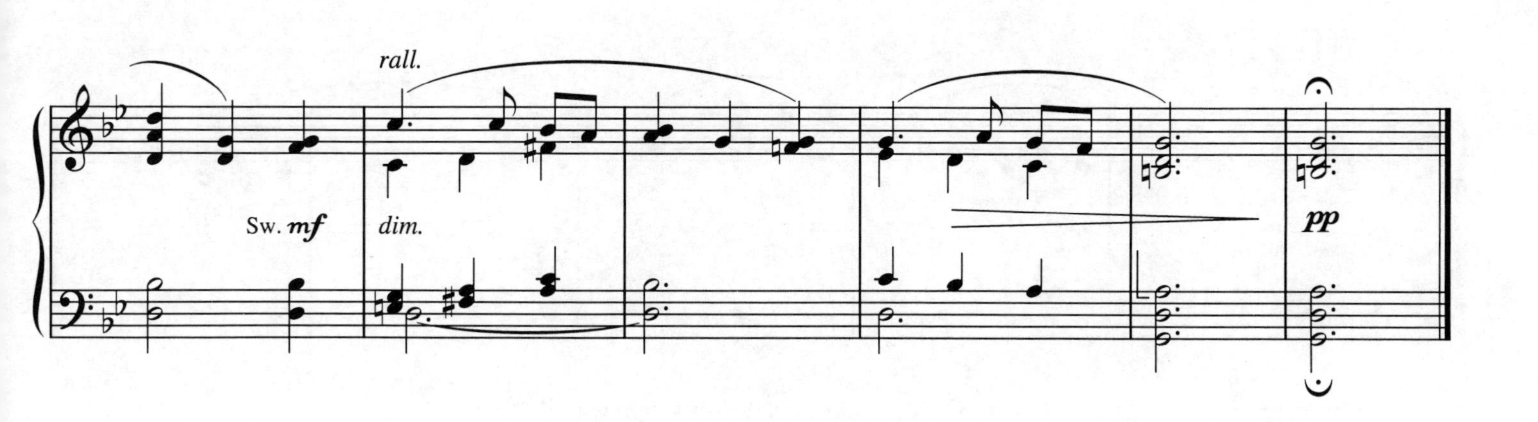
rall.
Sw. mf
dim.
pp

G MINOR

For Katharine and Maurice

Interlude 70

Betty Roe

A♭ MAJOR

Interlude 71

John Marsh

A♭ MAJOR

Interlude 72

Michael Higgins

Interlude 73

David Terry

A♭ MAJOR

Interlude 74

Andrew Wright

A♭ MAJOR

Interlude 75

Richard Lloyd

A MAJOR

Interlude 76

Andrew Fletcher

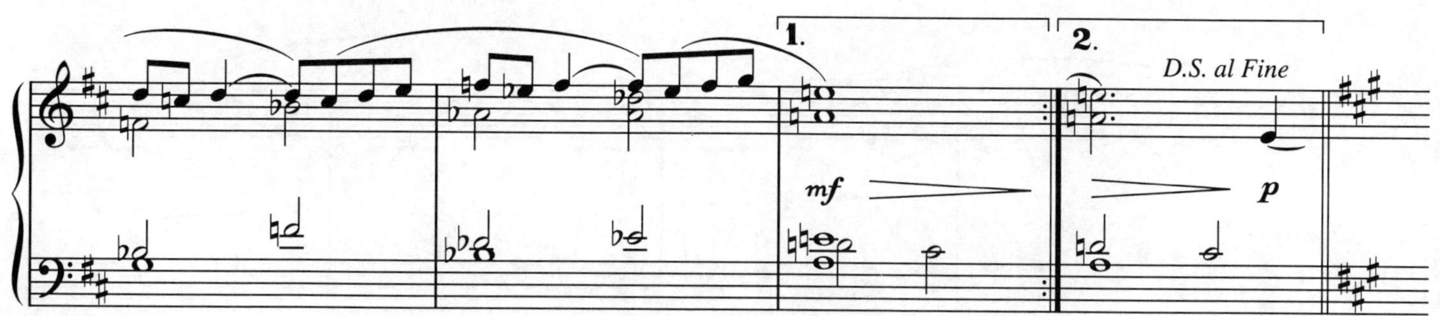

A MAJOR

To Fr. Paul Kish

Interlude 77

Malcolm McKelvey

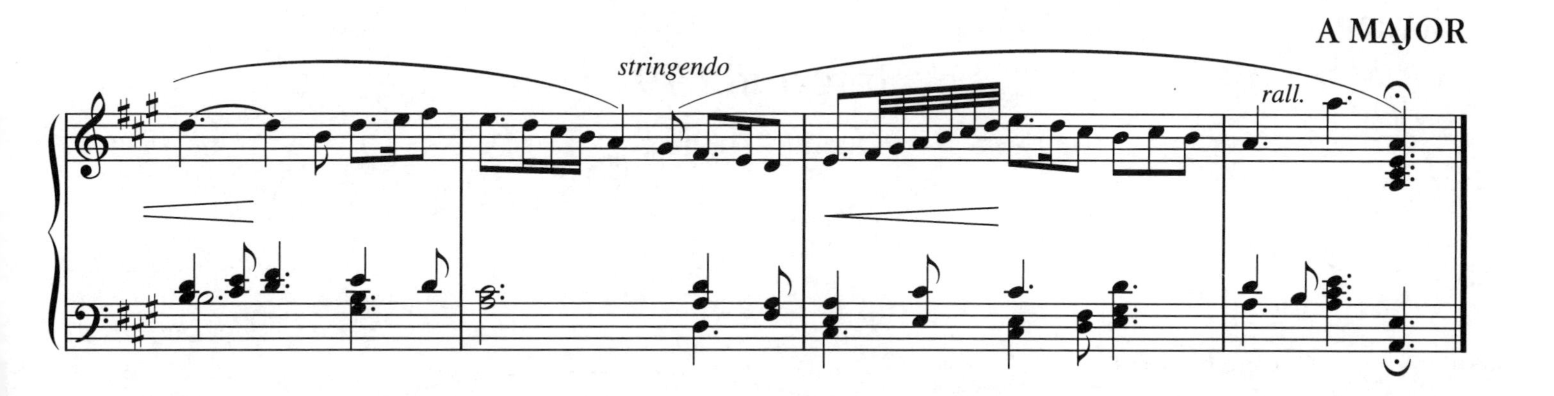

Interlude 78

Alan Rees

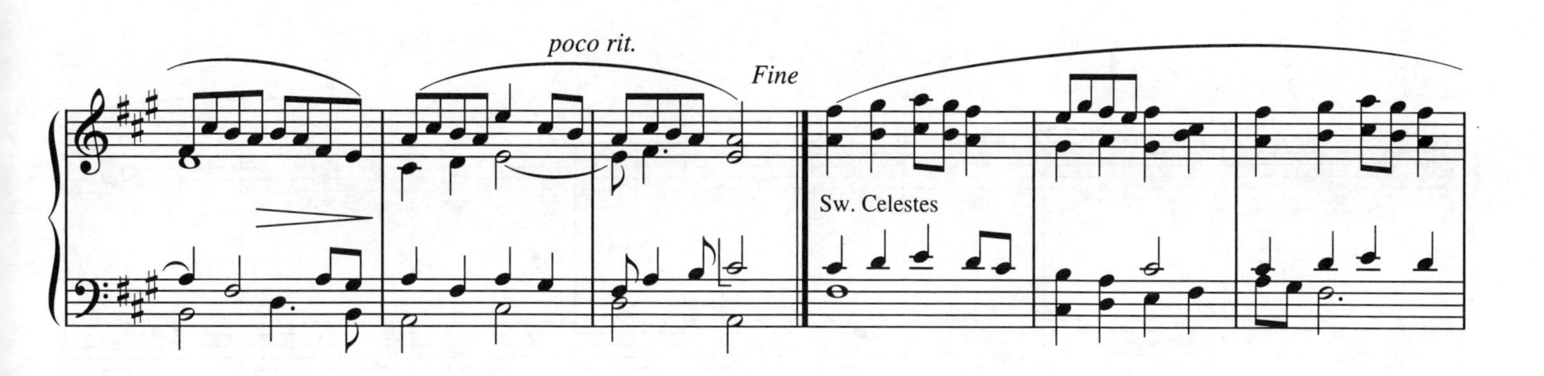

A MAJOR

Interlude 79

Quentin Thomas

A MINOR

Interlude 80

John Marsh

A MINOR

Interlude 81

Colin Hand

A MINOR

A MINOR

Interlude 82

Michael Higgins

Interlude 83

David Terry

A MINOR

Interlude 84

Elizabeth Hill

mp

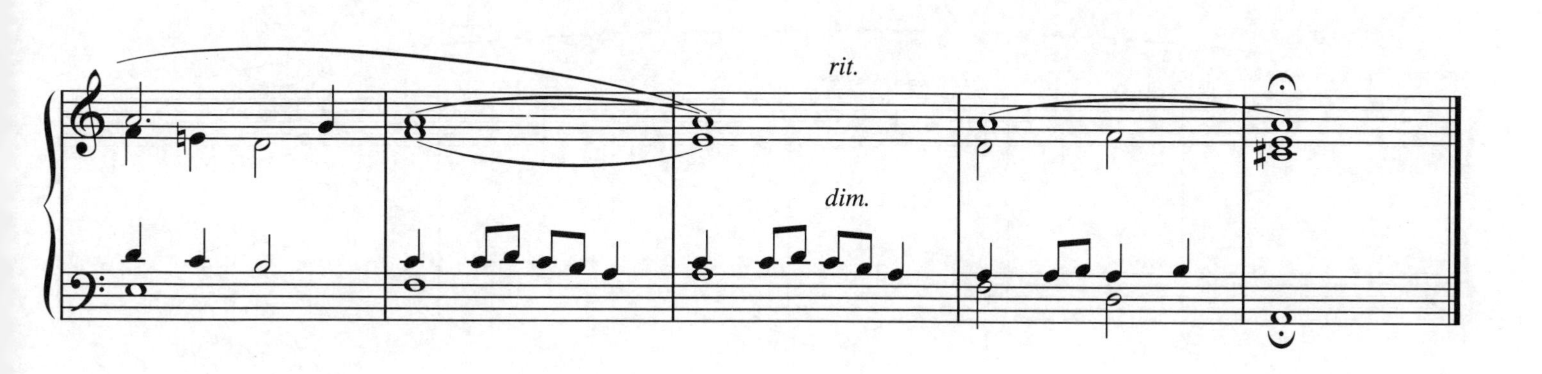
rit.
dim.

A MINOR

Interlude 85

Andrew Wright

A MINOR

Interlude 86

Richard Lloyd

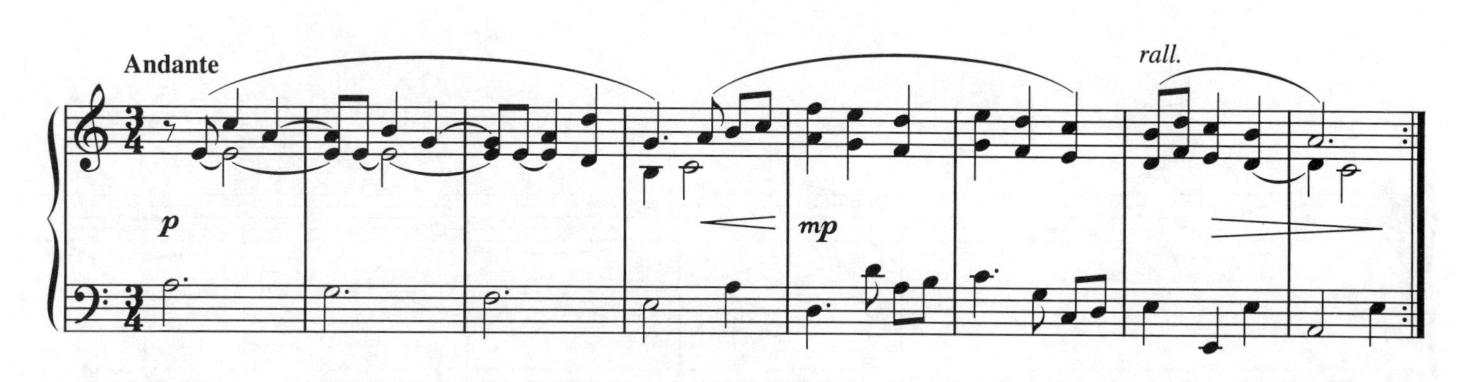

B♭ MAJOR

Interlude 87

David Terry

B♭ MAJOR

Interlude 88

Michael Higgins

Interlude 89

Colin Mawby

mp
mf
rit.
mp
p
pp

Interlude 90

Colin Hand

cresc.
mp
poco rit.
a tempo
dim.
rall.
p

B♭ MAJOR

Interlude 91

Elizabeth Hill

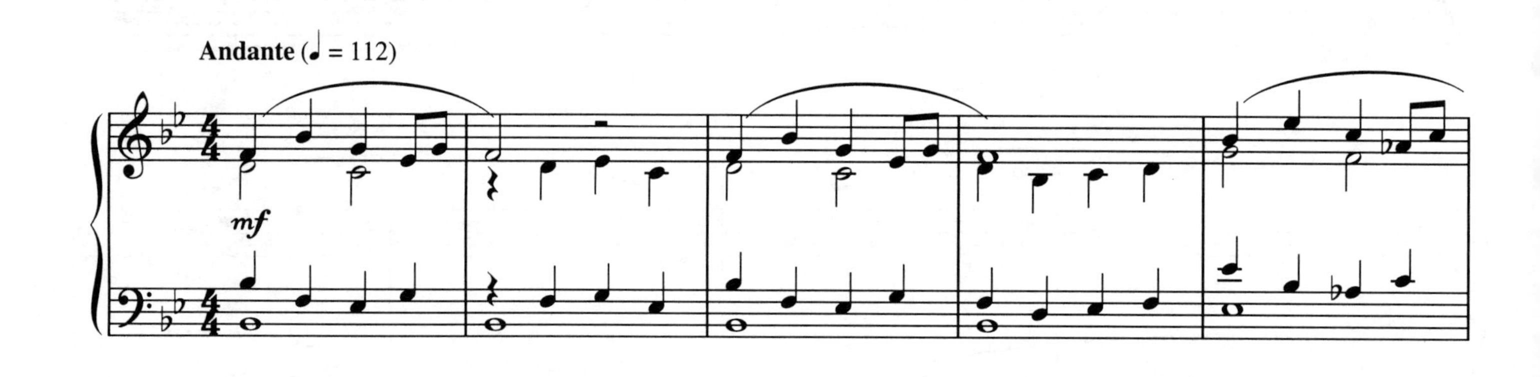

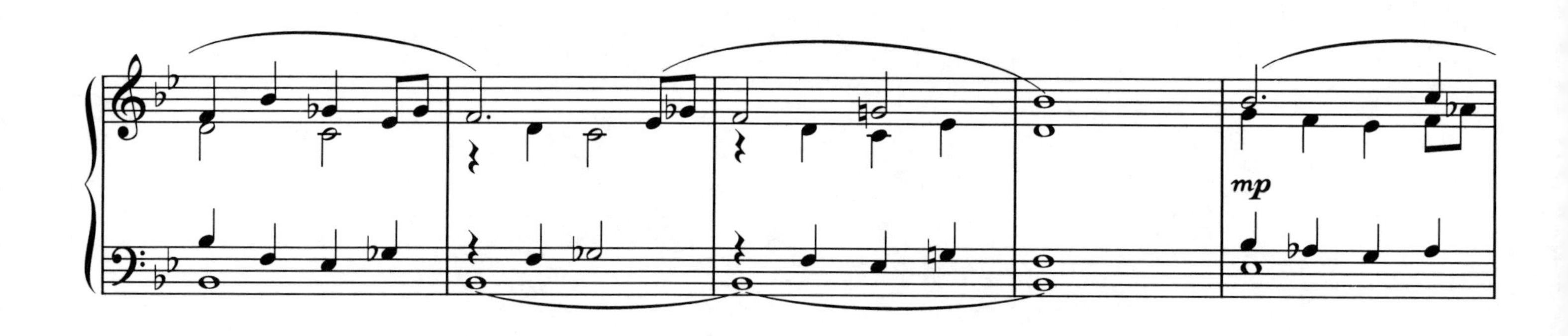

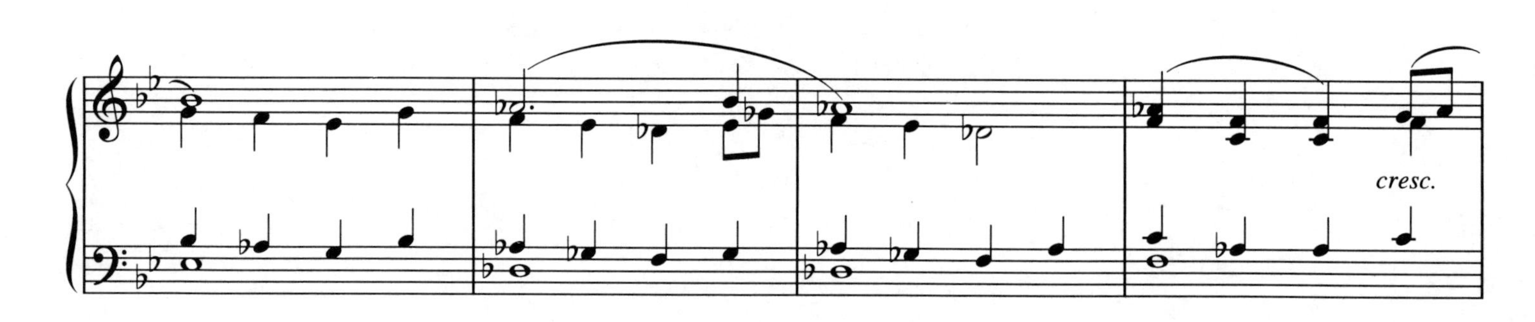

B♭ MAJOR

Interlude 92

Stanley Vann

Interlude 93

Richard Lloyd

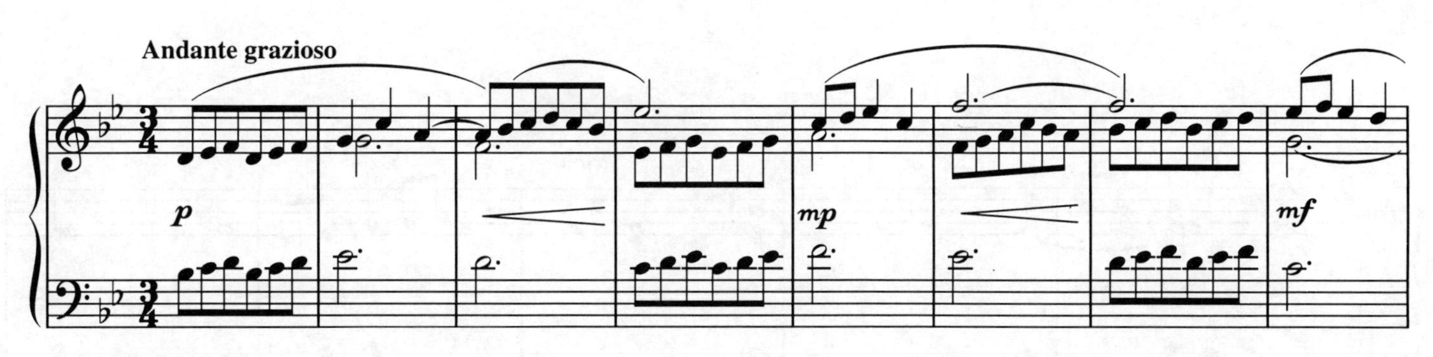

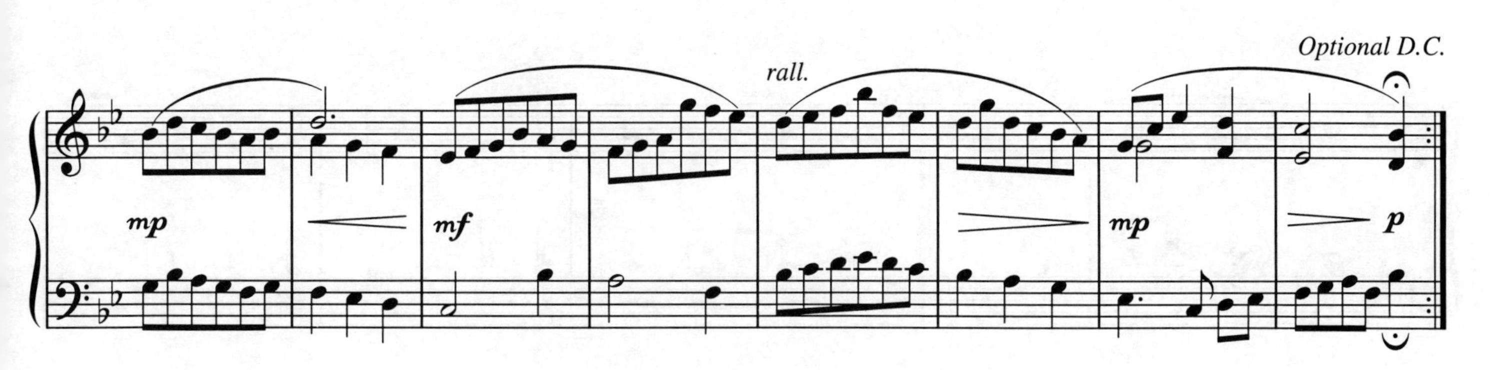

B MINOR

Interlude 94

John Marsh

For Katharine and Maurice

Interlude 95

Betty Roe

B MINOR

Interlude 96

June Nixon

Interlude 97

David Terry

B MINOR

Interlude 98

Norman Warren

B MINOR

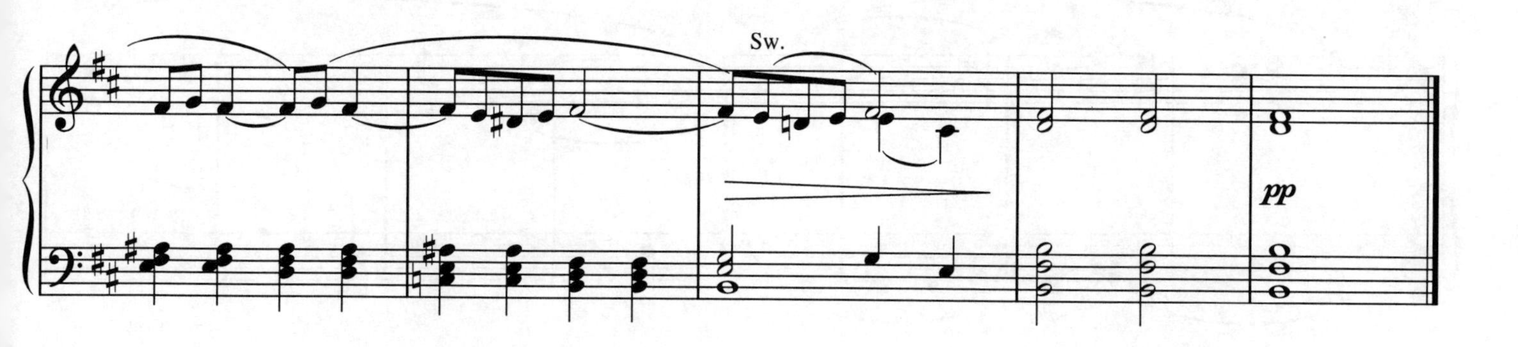

B MINOR

Interlude 99

Andrew Wright

D.C. al Fine

Interlude 100

Robert Jones

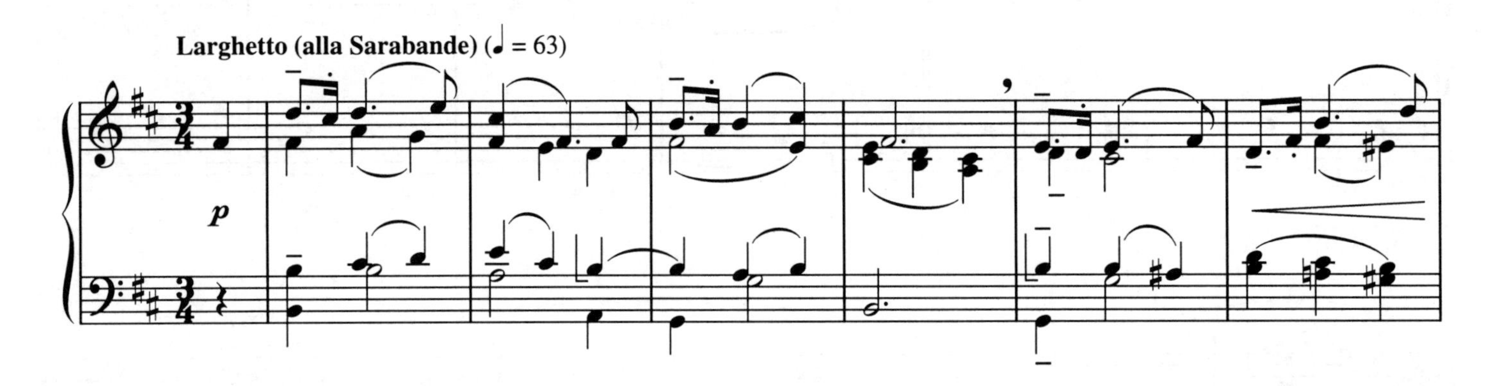

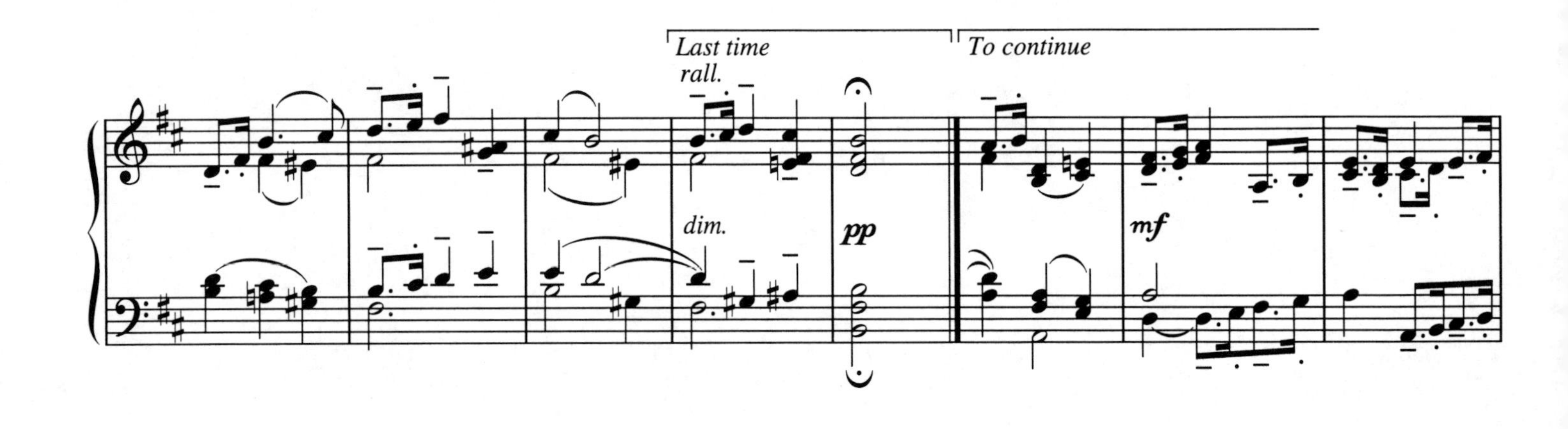